Annie, Bea, and Chi Chi Dolores

A SCHOOL DAY ALPHABET

by Donna Maurer   pictures by Denys Cazet

SCHOLASTIC INC.

New York   Toronto   London   Auckland   Sydney

Text copyright © 1993 by Donna Maurer.
Illustrations copyright © 1993 by Denys Cazet.
All rights reserved. Published by Scholastic Inc., 555 Broadway,
New York, NY 10012, by arrangement with Orchard Books.
Book design by Mina Greenstein.
Printed in the U.S.A.
ISBN 0-590-61737-0

2 3 4 5 6 7 8 9 10   14   02 01 00 99 98 97 96

The text of this book is set in 54 point Futura Book.
The illustrations are watercolor paintings reproduced in full color.

For my parents,
Sylvester and Virginia Maurer

—D.M.

A a
all aboard

B b
buddies

C c
counting

D d
drawing

E e erasing

F f   follow the leader

G g
giggling

H h
hopping

13

I i
icky

J j jumping rope

K k kicking a ball

L l   lining up

M m   making music

N n   noisy

O o

oops . . .

P p　　　painting

Q q
quiet

R r
running races

S s snack time

T t
tickling

U u
untangling

V v
vamoose

W w
whispering

X x
x-ing

29

Y y   yawning

Z z

zip